WHERE
BIRDS
SING

compiled by
Ada L. F. Snell
illustrated by
Freda Reiter

BOOKMAN ASSOCIATES

NEW YORK 3, N. Y.

FOTOSET BY ACADEMY PHOTO-OFFSET, INC., NEW YORK CITY, N. Y.
MANUFACTURED IN THE UNITED STATES OF AMERICA
NOBLE OFFSET PRINTERS, INC., NEW YORK, N. Y.

ACKNOWLEDGEMENTS

The compiler sincerely and gratefully thanks authors and publishers who have permitted the use in this collection of copyright material. Acknowledgement is made individually in the notes.

Very special indebtedness for many poems is due to The Bird Lovers Anthology compiled by Clinton Scollard and Jessie B. Rittenhouse, Houghton Mifflin Company, a book any bird-lover should own.

INTRODUCTION

Come were the spring many of us would like to go where birds sing but we have to go to school or to work, or we live in towns and cities. For such ones these poems have been gathered.   The number of birds in English literature is fairly limited. They hardly appear at all until modern times except in a stanza or two dedicated to some spiritually significant theme, as in Shelley's Skylark or Keat's Ode to a Nightingale.   It is hoped that with this book in hand, come any season anywhere, one may now and then see and hear as in early April a bluebird, or in late autumn a little voice singing chickadee dee dee!   Come again then the spring one may listen with added joy to birds singing in bush and tree. Victor Hugo goes a little further and exhorts the human to be like the bird which if on too slight a limb, feels it give way, still sings "knowing he hath wings."

CONTENTS

WHERE
BIRDS
SING

Gone were but the Winter
  Come were the Spring,
I would go to a covert
  Where the birds sing.
               Christina Rossetti

THE BIRD AT DAWN

If no man had invented human word
And a bird-song had been
The only way to utter what we mean,
What would we men have heard,
What understood, what seen,
Between the trills and pauses, in between
The singing and silence of a bird!

Harold Monro

L'OISEAU BLEU

The lake lay blue below the hill.
   O'er it, as I looked, there flew
Across the waters, cold and still,
   A bird whose wings were palest blue.

The sky above was blue at last,
   The sky beneath me blue in blue.
A moment, ere the bird had passed,
   It caught his image as he flew.
                 Mary Coleridge

THE ROBIN

The robin is the one
That interrupts the morn
With hurried, few, express reports
When March is scarcely on.

The robin is the one
That overflows the noon
With her cherubic quantity,
And April but begun.

The robin is the one
That speechless from her nest
Submits that home and certainty
And sanctity are best.

Emily Dickinson

THE BLUEBIRD

Before you thought of spring,
Except as a surmise,
You see, God bless his suddenness,
A fellow in the skies
Of independent hues,
A little weather-worn,
Inspiriting habiliments
Of indigo and brown.

With specimens of song,
As if for you to choose,
Discretion in the interval,
With gay delays he goes
To some superior tree
Without a single leaf,
And shouts for joy to nobody
But his seraphic self!

Emily Dickinson

I WATCHED A BLACKBIRD

I watched a blackbird on a budding sycamore
One Easter Day, when sap was stirring twigs to the core;
I saw his tongue, and crocus-coloured bill
Parting and closing as he turned his trill;
Then he flew down, seized on a stem of hay,
And upped to where his building scheme was under way,
As if so sure a nest were never shaped on spray.

Thomas Hardy

THE SWALLOWS

Gallant and gay in their doublets gray,
   All at a flash like the darting of a flame,
Chattering Arabic, African, Italian . . .
   Certain of springtime, the swallows came!

Doublets of gray silk and surcoats of purple,
   And ruffs of russet round each little throat,
Wearing such garb they had crossed the waters,
   Mariners sailing never a boat.

Edwin Arnold

THE WOODPECKER

The woodpecker pecked out a little round hole
And made him a house in a telephone pole.

One day when I watched, he poked out his head,
And he had on a hood and a collar red.

When the streams of rain pour out of the sky,
And the sparkles of lightning go flashing by,

And the big, BIG wheels of thunder roll,
He can snuggle back into the pole.

Elizabeth Madox Roberts

TWO PEWITS

Under the after-sunset sky
Two pewits sport and cry,
More white than is the moon on high
Riding the dark surge silently;
More black than earth. Their cry
Is the one sound under the sky.
They alone move, now low, now high,
And merrily they cry
To the mischievous spring sky,
Plunging earthward, tossing high,
Over the ghost who wonders why
So merrily they cry and fly,
Nor choose 'twixt earth and sky,
While the moon's quarter silently
Rides, and earth rests as silently.

Edward Thomas

TO A PHOEBE BIRD

Under the eaves, out of the wet,
   You nest within my reach;
You never sing for me and yet
   You have a golden speech.

You sit and quirk a rapid tail,
   Wrinkle a ragged crest,
Then pirouette from tree to rail
   And vault from rail to nest.

And when in frequent, dainty fright
   You gayly slip and fade,
And when at hand you re-alight
   Demure and unafraid,

And when you bring your brood its fill
   Of iridescent wings
And green legs dewy in your bill,
   Your silence is what sings.

Not of a feather that enjoys
   To prate or praise or preach,
O phoebe, with so little noise,
   What eloquence you teach!

                    Witter Bynner

REDBIRDS

Redbirds, redbirds,
  Long and long ago,
What a honey-call you had
  In hills I used to know!

Redbud, buckberry,
  Wild plum-tree
And proud river sweeping
  Southward to the sea,

Brown and gold in the sun
  Sparkling far below,
Trailing stately round her bluffs
  Where the poplars grow—

Redbirds, redbirds,
  Are you singing still
As you sang one May day
  On Saxton's Hill?

Sara Teasdale

MOCKING BIRD

An arrow, feathery, alive,
   He darts and sings—
Then with a sudden skimming dive
   Of striped wings
He finds a pine and, debonair,
   Makes with his mate
All birds that ever rested there
   Articulate.

The whisper of a multitude
   Of happy wings
Is round him, a returning brood,
   Each time he sings . . .
Though Heaven be not for them or him
   Yet he is wise,
And tiptoes daily on the rim
   Of Paradise.

Witter Bynner

BLUE JAY

I hear a savage tale of you,
Raucous of voice, magnificently blue.
Cannibal bird! Whose dark, defiant note
Is answered from another throat
As bright, though out of sight.

Along the icy bough you swing,
Apostrophizing a belated spring;
And I seem not to mind
Those horrid deeds to smaller of your kind:
For as you fly,
You scatter color through a frozen sky.

Black-hearted is your breast—
But ah, the blue of that uplifted crest!

Leonora Speyer

THE LITTLE BROWN WREN

There's a little brown wren that has built in our tree,
And she's scarcely as big as a bumblebee;
She has hollowed a house in the heart of a limb,
And made the walls tidy and made the floor trim
With the down of the crow's foot, with tow and with straw,
The coziest dwelling that you ever saw.

The little brown wren has the brightest of eyes,
And a foot of a very diminutive size;
Her tail is as big as the sail of a ship;
She's demure, though she walks with a hop and skip;
And her voice,—but a flute were more fit than a pen
To tell of the voice of the little brown wren.

One morning Sir Sparrow came sauntering by,
And cast on the wren's nest an envious eye;
With a strut of bravado and a toss of his head
"I'll put in my claim here," that bold fellow said.
So, straightway, he mounted on impudent wing,
And entered the door without pausing to ring.

An instant,—and swiftly that feathery knight,
All towsled and tumbled, in terror took flight,
While there by the door on her favorite perch,
As neat as a lady just starting for church,
With this song on her lips, "He will not call again,
Unless he is asked," said the little brown wren.

Clinton Scollard

THE WHITE OWL

When cats run home and light is come,
  And dew is cold upon the ground,
And the far-off stream is dumb,
  And the whirring sail goes round,
  And the whirring sail goes round;
    Alone and warming his five wits,
    The white owl in the belfry sits.

When merry milkmaids click the latch,
  And rarely smells the new-mown day,
And the cock hath sung beneath the thatch
  Twice or thrice his roundelay,
  Twice or thrice his roundelay;
    Alone and warming his five wits,
    The white owl in the belfry sits.

                    Alfred Tennyson

THE WISE THRUSH

And after April, when May follows
And the whitethroat builds, and all the swallows—
Hush! where my blossomed pear-tree in the hedge
   Leans to the field and scatters on the clover
Blossoms and dewdrops—at the bent spray's edge—
   That's the wise thrush; he sings each song twice over
Lest you should think he never could recapture
The first fine careless rapture!

Robert Browning

THE WHIPPOORWILL

Do you remember, father,—
  It seems so long ago,—
The day we fished together
  Along the Pocono?
At dusk I waited for you,
  Beside the lumber-mill,
And there I heard a hidden bird
  That chanted, "whip-poor-will,"
  "Whippoorwill! whippoorwill!"
  Sad and shrill,—"whippoorwill!"

The place was all deserted;
  The mill-wheel hung at rest;
The lonely star of evening
  Was quivering in the west;
The veil of night was falling;
  The winds were folded still;
And everywhere the trembling air
  Re-echoed "whip-poor-will!"
  "Whippoorwill! whippoorwill!"
  Sad and shrill,—"whippoorwill!"

You seemed so long in coming,
  I felt so much alone;
The wide, dark world was round me,
  And life was all unknown;
The hand of sorrow touched me,
  And made my senses thrill
With all the pain that haunts the strain
  Of mournful whip-poor-will.
  "Whippoorwill! whippoorwill!"
  Sad and shrill,—"whippoorwill!"

What did I know of trouble?
  An idle little lad;
I had not learned the lessons
  That make men wise and sad.
I dreamed of grief and parting,
  And something seemed to fill
My heart with tears, while in my ears
  Resounded "whip-poor-will."
  "Whippoorwill! whippoorwill!"
  Sad and shrill,—"whippoorwill!"

'Twas but a shadowy sadness,
  That lightly passed away;
But I have known the substance
  Of sorrow, since that day,
For nevermore at twilight,
  Beside the silent mill,
I'll wait for you, in the falling dew,
  And hear the whip-poor-will.
  "Whippoorwill! whippoorwill!"
  Sad and shrill,—"whippoorwill!"

But if you still remember,
  In that fair land of light,
The pains and fears that touch us
  Along this edge of night,
I think all earthly grieving,
  And all our mortal ill,
To you must seem like a boy's sad dream,
  Who hears the whip-poor-will.
  "Whippoorwill! whippoorwill!"
  A passing thrill—"whippoorwill!"

                              H. Van Dyke

WOOD FINCHES

So the wood finches too,
  Though timely tamed they be,
If to the woods escaped anew,
  Again they flutter free;

They will not leave the wood,
Though by their trainers, as of yore,
Enticed by tempting food;
  So merry seem the trees;
  That meats no more may please.
All winsome then is found
  The wild wood sounding strong
With other birds that sing around,
  Stunning one's ears with noise
  Of their woodland joys.
                    Boethius
                        translated by Martin F. Tupper

THE SWAN

Hawks stir the blood like fiercely ringing bells
Or far-off bugles;
Even on their perches
They are all latent fury and sheathed power;
And peacocks trail the glory of the world.
But calm, white calm, was born into a swan
To float forever upon moon-smoothed waters
Cool placid breast against cool mirrored breast
And wings curved like great petals
And long throat
Bent dreamily
To listen to the ripple
That widens slowly in a tranquil arrow
Reaching the shores, and lisping on the sand.

Elizabeth Coatsworth

DUCKS' DITTY

All along the backwater,
Through the rushes tall,
Ducks are a-dabbling,
Up tails all!

Ducks' tails, drakes' tails,
Yellow feet a-quiver,
Yellow bills all out of sight
Busy in the river!

Slushy green undergrowth
Where the roach swim
Here we keep our larder,
Cool and full and dim.

Every one for what he likes!
We like to be
Heads down, tails up,
Dabbling free!

High in the blue above
Swifts whirl and call
We are down a-dabbling,
Up tails all!

Kenneth Grahame

THE SANDPIPER

Along the sea-edge, like a gnome
Or rolling pebble in the foam,
As though he timed the ocean's throbbing,
Runs a piper, bobbing, bobbing.

Now he stiffens, now he wilts,
Like a little boy on stilts!
Creatures burrow, insects hide,
When they see the piper glide.

You would think him out of joint,
Till his bill began to point.
You would doubt if he could fly,
Till his straightness arrows by.

You would take him for a clown,
Till he peeps and flutters down,
Vigilant among the grasses,
Where a fledgling bobs and passes.

Witter Bynner

THE BITTERN

If you see a bittern,
A tall brown bittern
That walks among the weeds
Where the sunny water
Lies without a ripple,
Where the little frogs are reared,
But always fearfully—
A green-legged bittern
Wading, he will be
Looking for worms and water-bugs,
Eating them quietly,
And if he hears the merest stir—
If anyone should pass—
He'll throw back his head
And look like the grass.

                    Roberta Teale Swartz

PIGEONS

At morning the pale pigeons come in a band,
Shining and fleet, descending lightly where
I walk through red metallic tulips grown
High in the yellow air.

When they are here my garden is never my own.
I am a newcomer in a silent land.
And after I have gone the birds will run
About, the tulips stand.

The level breeze is silent in the sun
The beautiful birds flock down; I cannot bear
Their folded ivory wings, I cannot ponder
Their hard incurious stare.

They peck possessive on the ground. I wander
Slow and persistent over grass and stone
Softly to scatter them until they lift
And I am left alone.

They go forgot in sky, but they will drift
Together downward and sink suddenly
To flutter at my feet like blossoms blown
From a high windy tree.

George Dillon

CATBIRD

Who can be that somber fellow
Garbed in gray?
Is it Puck or Punchinello
Perched upon a birchen spray?
Eyes that gleam and eyes that glisten,
(Listen, listen,
While he runs his gamut through!)
He's the minstrel of the thicket,
Chirk and cheery as a cricket
Although clad in sober hue.

Spry—no fairy could be spryer—
As he tunes his airy lyre;
Merry, mellow avalanches
Toss and tumble from the branches;
All his trills and all his trebles,
Like a rillet over pebbles,
He is tricky
As a pixy,
This gay feathered troubadour.
Stephen Crombie

HUMMINGBIRD

Prism in sunlight,
  Swiftly turned,
  Flashes no colors
  Such as burned
  Flamebright and instant
  When you whirred
  Over the larkspur.
  Hummingbird!
Elizabeth Palmer

TO AN ORIOLE

How falls it, Oriole, thou has come to fly
In tropic splendor through our Northern sky?

At some glad moment was it Nature's choice
To dower a scrap of sunset with a voice?

Or did some orange tulip, flaked with black,
In some forgotten garden, ages back,

Yearning toward Heaven until its wish was heard
Desire unspeakably to be a bird?

Edgar Fawc

THE WOOD THRUSH

When lilies by the river fill with snow,
And banks with clemates are overrun;
When winds are weighted with fern-sweet from the hill,
And hawks wheel in the noontide hot and still;
When thistle-tops are silvered, every one,
And fly-lamps, flicker ere the day is done,
Nature orthinks her how to crown her things,—
At twilight she decides: the wood-thrush sings.—

John Vance Cheney

GOLDFINCHES

Now that the giant sunflowers rise
  Along the garden way,
The shy goldfinches, seeking seeds,
  Visit them through the day.

One fancies as one watches them
  And hears their low refrain
That they are sunbeams changed to birds
  That seek the sun again.

Elizabeth Scollard

ROBERT OF LINCOLN

Merrily swinging on brier and weed,
  Near to the nest of his little dame,
Over the mountain-side or mead,
  Robert of Lincoln is telling his name:
    Bob-o'-link, bob-o'-link,
    Spink, spank, spink;
Snug and safe is that nest of ours,
Hidden among the summer flowers.
                Chee, chee, chee.

Robert of Lincoln is gayly dressed,
  Wearing a bright black wedding-coat;
White are his shoulders and white his crest.
  Hear him call in his merry note:
    Bob-o'-link, bob-o'-link,
    Spink, spank, spink;
Look, what a nice new coat is mine,
Sure there was never a bird so fine.
                Chee, chee, chee.

Robert of Lincoln's Quaker wife,
    Pretty and quiet, with plain brown wings,
Passing at home a patient life,
    Broods in the grass while her husband sings;
        Bob-o'-link, bob-o'-link,
        Spink, spank, spink;
Brood, kind creature, you need not fear
Thieves and robbers while I am here.
                    Chee, chee, chee.

Modest and shy as a nun is she;
    One weak chirp is her only note.
Braggart and prince of braggarts is he,
    Pouring boasts from his little throat:
        Bob-o'-link, bob-o'-link,
        Spink, spank, spink;
Never was I afraid of man;
Catch me, cowardly knaves, if you can!
                    Chee, chee, chee.

Six white eggs on a bed of hay,
    Flecked with purple, a pretty sight!
There as the mother sits all day,
    Robert is singing with all his might:
        Bob-o'-link, bob-o'-link,
        Spink, spank, spink;
Nice good wife, that never goes out,
Keeping house while I frolic about.
                    Chee, chee, chee.

Soon as the little ones chip the shell,
    Six wide mouths are open for food;
Robert of Lincoln bestirs him well,
    Gathering seeds for the hungry brood.
        Bob-o'-link, bob-o'-link,
        Spink, spank, spink;
This new life is likely to be
Hard for a gay young fellow like me.
                    Chee, chee, chee.

Robert of Lincoln at length is made
   Sober with work, and silent with care;
Off his holiday garment laid,
   Half forgotten that merry air:
     Bob-o'-link, bob-o'-link,
     Spink, spank, spink;
Nobody knows but my mate and I
Where our nest and our nestlings lie.
                Chee, chee, chee.

Summer wanes; the children are grown;
   Fun and frolic no more he knows;
Robert of Lincoln's a humdrum crone;
   Off he flies, and we sing as he goes:
     Bob-o'-link, bob-o'-link,
     Spink, spank, spink;
When you can pipe that merry old strain,
Robert of Lincoln, come back again.
                Chee, chee, chee.
             William Cullen Bryant

BOB WHITE

Look! the valleys are thick with grain
  Heavy and tall;
Peaches drop in the heavy lane
  By the orchard wall;
Apples, streaked with a crimson stain,
  Bask in the sunshine, warm and bright:
Hark to the quail that pipes for rain—
  Bob White! Bob White!
Augur of mischief, pipes for rain—
  Bob White!

Men who reap on the fruitful plain
  Skirting the town,
Lift their eyes to the shifting vane
  As the sun goes down;
Slowly the farmer's loaded wain
  Climbs the slope in the failing light—
Bold is the voice that pipes for rain—
  Bob White! Bob White!
Still from the hillside, pipes for rain—
  Bob White!

Lo! a burst at the darkened pane,
   Angry and loud!
Waters murmur and winds complain
   To the rolling cloud;
Housed at the farm, the careless swain,
   Weaving snares while the fire burns bright,
Tuning his lips to the old refrain—
   Bob White! Bob White!
Oh, the sound of the blithe refrain—
   Bob White!

Dora Read Goodale

OVER IN THE MEADOW

Over in the meadow
In a nest built of sticks
Lived an old mother crow
And her little crows six.
Caw, said the mother
We caw, said the six
So they cawed all day
In a nest built of sticks.
Old Nursery Poem

CROW

A hundred autumns he has wheeled
Above this solitary field.
Here he circled after corn
Before the oldest man was born.
When the oldest man is dead,
He will be unsurfeited.
See him crouch upon a limb
With his banquet under him.
Hear the echo of his caw
Give the skirting forest law.
Down he drops, and struts among
The rows of supper, tassel-hung.
Not a grain is left behind
That his polished beak can find.

He is full; he rises slow
To watch the evening come and go.
From the barren branch, his rest,
All is open to the west;
And the light along his wing
Is a sleek and oily thing.
Past an island floats the gaze
Of this ancientest of days.
Green and orange and purple dye
Is reflected in his eye.
There is an elm-tree in the wood
Where his dwelling-place has stood
All the hundreds of his years.
There he sails and disappears.

Mark Van Doren

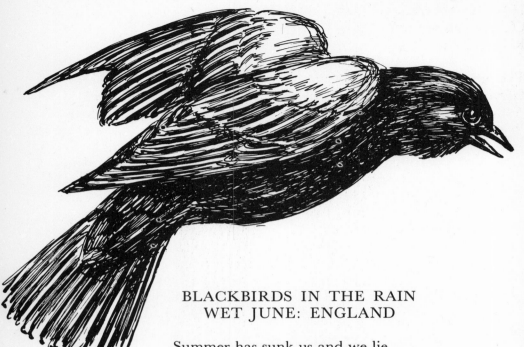

BLACKBIRDS IN THE RAIN
WET JUNE: ENGLAND

Summer has sunk us and we lie
Under the heaps and mounds of may,
Petals like pence upon our eyes,
Lungs stopped with leaves, yet while we drown
Among the weeds and twines of hay,
Among the hulks and wrecks of May,
We hear above our going down
The choirschool blackbirds high and dry,
Chanting no *Dirige,* but *Hey*
Nonny nonny above the may—
      cocks, the treetops, the always falling sky.

Joyce Horner

THE EAGLE

He clasps the crag with crooked hands;
Close to the sun in lonely lands,
Ringed with the azure world, he stands.

The wrinkled sea beneath him crawls;
He watches from his mountain walls,
And like a thunderbolt he falls.

Alfred Tennyson

WINTER BIRDS

There was no covert for the birds
  And yet I heard them sing
As joyously as if the trees
  Were canopied with spring.

And though the way is still obscure
  That you and I must go,
Yet all my hopes, like winter birds,
  Sing on amid the snow.
                    Elinor MacArthur

TO A SPARROW

Because you have no fear to mingle
Wings with those of greater part,
So like me, your song I single,
Your sweet impudence of heart.

And when prouder feathers go where
Summer holds her leafy show,
You still come to us from nowhere
Like gray leaves across the snow.

In back ways where odd and end go,
To your meals you drop down sure,
Knowing every broken window
Of the hospitable poor.

There is no bird half so harmless
None so sweetly rude as you,
None so common and so charmless,
None of virtues nude as you.

But for all your faults I love you,
For you linger with us still,
Though the wintry winds reprove you,
And the snow is on the hill.

Francis Ledwidge

CHICKADEE

There's a hush on the frosty furrow where the frozen
    loam lifts black,
And a film on the brown hare's burrow unmarred by a
    seeking track,
And over the leafless uplands comes echoing clear to me
A voice from the edge of winter:
       "Chickadee dee dee! Chickadee!"

The fox has slunk from the bracken with the flag of his
    tail dropped low,
And the whining bound-winds slacken at the first soft
    swirl of snow,
But still from the wind-blown whiteness comes cheerily
    back to me
A gay little voice from the pine-top:
       "Chickadee dee dee! Chickadee!"

Oh, little gray Pick undaunted when the fields lie white
    and still,
May ever my pane be haunted by your voice at my
    window-sill,
The cheeriest note of winter comes rollicking oft to me
Like the voice of a song-struck sunbeam:
       "Chickadee dee dee! Chickadee!"
                    Martha Haskell Clark

SOMETHING TOLD THE WILD GEESE

Something told the wild geese
   It was time to go.
Though the fields lay golden
   Something whispered,—"Snow."

Leaves were green and stirring
   Berries, luster-glossed,
But beneath warm feathers
   Something cautioned,—"Frost."

All the sagging orchards
   Steam with amber spice.
But each wild beast stiffened
   At remembered ice.

Something told the wild geese,
   It was time to fly,—
Summer sun was on their wings,
   Winter in their cry.

Rachel Field

THE LAST WORD OF A BLUEBIRD
AS TOLD TO A CHILD

As I went out a Crow
In a low voice said Oh,
I was looking for you.
How do you do?
I just came to tell you
To tell Lesley (will you?)
That her little Bluebird
Wanted me to bring word
That the north wind last night
That made the stars bright
And made ice on the trough
Almost made him cough
His tail feathers off.
He just had to fly!
But he sent her Good-bye,
And said to be good,
And wear her red hood,
And look for skunk tracks
In the snow with an axe—
And do everything!
And perhaps in the spring
He would come back and sing!

Robert Frost

NOTES

THE BIRD AT DAWN. Harold Monro, 1879-1932. Established the poetry book shop in London and the magazine Poetry Review.

L'OISEAU BLEU. Mary Coleridge, 1861-1907, great niece of Samuel T. Coleridge. She taught in the Working Womens College.

I WATCHED A BLACKBIRD. Thomas Hardy, 1840-1929, from Winter Birds. The Macmillan Company. William Henley writes of the blackbird as follows:

> "The nightingale has a lyre of gold,
>   The lark a clarion call,
> And a blackbird plays but a boxwood flute,
>   But I love him best of all!"

THE SWALLOWS. Sir Edwin Arnold, 1832-1904. English poet famous for the Light of Asia. Of the swallows nest building he writes:

> "Day after day her nest she moulded,
>   Building with magic, love and mud,
> A gray cup made of a thousand journeys,
>   And the tiny beak was trowel and hod."

John Burroughs says of swallows their call "crowns the vernal year"—makes it clear spring has come. Voice of barn swallows is a soft kuik-wit-wit.

THE WOODPECKER. Elizabeth Madox Roberts, from Under the Tree. By permission of The Viking Press, New York.

TO A PHOEBE BIRD. Witter Bynner, from Grenstone Poems, by permission Alfred A. Knopf. The bird is noted for its persistent tail-wagging. It arrives in early spring, builds nest near-by; comes back year after year to same place; —very useful since it eats destructive insects. Song, bee-bee.

REDBIRDS. Sara Teasdale, 1884-1933. From Flame and Shadow, by permission Macmillan Company. Voice is a clear slurred whistle, what-cheer, cheer, cheer, what cheer.

MOCKING BIRD. Witter Bynner, from Verse of Our Day, by permission of Alfred A. Knopf.

THE BLUE JAY. Leonora Speyer, 1872-1956, by permission of Events Publishing Co. Miss Speyer was a teacher at Columbia University. Voice of bird, a harsh geerk-jay-jay, also other notes. Called a creature of iniquity.

THE LITTLE BROWN WREN. Clinton Scollard, 1860-1932. Poet, with many volumes of verse. Was Professor of English at Hamilton College. Voice of the bird a high, trembling warble ending on a light trill-kip kip. The brown wren curls his tail over his back.

THE WHITE OWL. Alfred Lord Tennyson, 1809-1892. The title of this poem is When Cats Run Home. Poem published when he was 21 years old. The American owl is a long white bird, likes to perch on posts, "Firmly dight with feathers like a lady bright!" The English "Sweet Suffolk Owl with shrill command the mouse controls; and sings a dirge for dying souls!"

THE WISE THRUSH. Robert Browning. An English bird, its song is a phrase like "Did he do it?" Both American and English are heavily spotted, the English is darker in color, the American brownish with red head.

THE WHIPPOORWILL. Henry Van Dyke, 1852-1933. From Builders and Other Poems, 1897. Charles Scribner's Sons.

WOOD FINCHES. Boethius. Roman philosopher, 470-524, known for Consolations of Philosophy. Song similar to that of the Goldfinch, a loud cheep-fip, also a light tit-i-tit, and a long buzzy skreel.

THE SWAN. Elizabeth Coatsworth, by permission of Harper and Brothers.

DUCKS' DITTY. Kenneth Grahame, from The Wind in the Willows, by permission Scribners.

THE SANDPIPER. Witter Bynner, by permission Alfred A. Knopf, from Grenstone Poems. Voice described as jee-jeet, jeet, "like the rasping of two pebbles."

THE BITTERN. Roberta Teale Swartz. Miss Swartz is the author of two volumes of poetry, Lord Juggler and Lilliput, a third ready for publication. The bittern lives in marshes, points bill upward; song described as a deep ooing ka-chunk,—from a distance sounds "like a mallet driving a stake in mud."

PIGEONS. George Dillon, from Boy in the Wind, by permission of The Viking Press, New York. H. H. Abbott describes pigeons as circling housetops and perching gravely upon chimney tops.

CATBIRD. Stephen Crombie. William Henry Venable describes the catbird song as hilarious rhapsody,—

> "Just to please himself and me!
> Primo Cantante!
> Scherzo! Andante!
> Piano pianissimo!"

TO AN ORIOLE. Edgar Fawcett, 1847-1904, by permission of Houghton Mifflin Company. American poet, novelist, and dramatist. From Poems for Older Children.

THE WOOD THRUSH. John Vance Cheney. The American thrush is smaller than a robin, lives in autumn woodlands, winters in Florida. Song a flute-like ee-o-lay. Call, a rapid pip, pip, pip. The English thrush is a darker bird, is said to dance in courting.

GOLDFINCHES. Elizabeth Scollard, by permission of Houghton Mifflin Company, from the Bird Lovers Anthology. The song of the goldfinch is described as clear, light and canary-like, sings in flight, each dip ends with a ti-dee-di-di.

ROBERT OF LINCOLN. William Cullen Bryant, 1794-1878. Two stanzas omitted. James Russell Lowell calls the bobolink "Gladness on wings . . . half-